Gold Stars®

Maths
and English
Activity Pad

Ages 5–

GW00374640

Written by Betty
Monica Hughes and I
Illustrated by Adam Linley.

Helping your child

⭐ Let your child know that you can share the activities. Talk about what's on the page.

⭐ Explain what has to be done on each page, and help with any recording such as colouring and joining up. Pencil control in young children is not usually very well developed.

⭐ Don't become anxious if your child finds any of the activities too difficult. Young children develop and learn at different rates. It's quite common to find children who seem not to want to learn, and who then suddenly put on a spurt once they are ready.

⭐ The answers to the activities start on page 92.

⭐ Always give your child lots of encouragement and praise.

⭐ Use the gold star stickers to reward effort as well as achievement.

Contents

All about me

Fill in the missing words.

 My name is _____

My age is _____

I live at _____

_____

_____

My school is called _____

 My favourite animal is _____

My favourite sport is _____

More about me

Draw yourself in the box.
Read the words and draw a line to the right part.

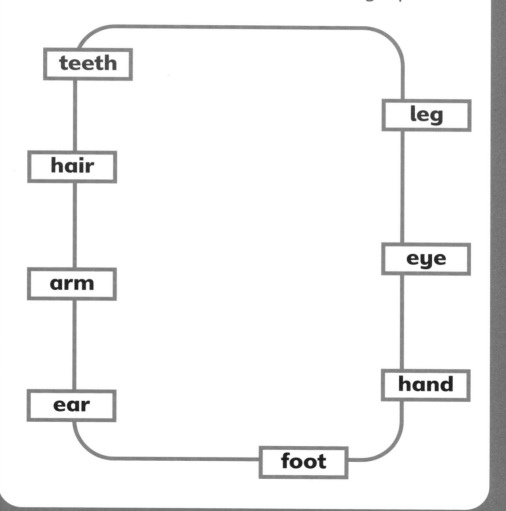

teeth

leg

hair

arm

eye

ear

hand

foot

Note for parent: This activity helps with
understanding parts of the body.

Middle sounds

Join the pictures that have the same middle sounds – **a**, **e**, **i**, **o** or **u**

$2+4=6$

Note for parent: Children have to listen very carefully to hear middle sounds. Be patient!

6

Middle vowels

Use the vowels **a**, **e**, **i**, **o** or **u** to complete
the words below.

b _ s

p _ g

m _ n

s _ ck

r _ d

cr _ b

j _ t

d _ ck

f _ sh

Note for parent: This activity gives children extra
practice in identifying middle sounds.

Odd one out

Cross out the picture in each row that does not belong.

Note for parent: This activity helps children to classify objects.

8

Silly or sensible?

Look at the picture. Read the sentences and put a tick next to the ones that are sensible.

The teacher is under the table. ____
A girl is reading a book. ____
A boy is painting the door. ____
The teacher is looking at the children. ____
A cat is reading a book. ____
A boy has got a brush. ____
The hamster is on its cage. ____

 Note for parent: This activity helps children to understand sentences and make the correct response.

9

Using labels

Read these words:

> **ball** **boy** **girl** **man** **car** **tree**

Now write the words in the boxes below.

Note for parent: This activity gives practice in matching words with pictures.

Double sounds

Look at these pictures and say each beginning sound.

bl br cl cr

Fill in the missing letters.

_ _ ock   _ _ idge   _ _ own   _ _ ack

Now do the same again.

dr   fl   gr   pl

_ _ een   _ _ ug   _ _ ill   _ _ ag

Note for parent: This activity helps children to learn these double beginning sounds: bl, br, cl, cr, dr, fl, gr and pl.

More doubles

Join the sounds to the pictures.

cl

dr

sn

bl

gr

sp

st

sw

 Note for parent: Here is another chance to learn double sounds.

12

The Enormous Turnip

Look at the pictures. Read the sentences.
Match each sentence to the correct picture.

Everyone fell over and the turnip came out. __

The farmer saw an enormous turnip. __

Everyone tried to pull up the turnip. __

The farmer tried to pull up the turnip. __

Note for parent: This activity gives practice in
reading for understanding.

How does it end?

Look at each row of pictures. Tell the story but choose the ending that you like the best.

or

or

or

 Note for parent: This activity gives children practice in telling a story from pictures.

14

Alphabetical order

a b c d e f g h i j k l m n o p q r s t u v w x y z

Write the beginning sound of each picture.
Then put the three letters in each row in
alphabetical order.

___ ___ ___

___ ___ ___

___ ___ ___

___ ___ ___

___ ___ ___

 Note for parent: Two skills are required for this activity:
knowing beginning sounds and alphabetical order.

Little words

Find each little word in one of the big words and then join them with a line.

or

us

an

all

am

in

at

fork

lamb

twins

bat

man

ball

bus

How many of the little words can you read? _____

Note for parent: It is great fun to find words inside other words.

16

Find the right word

sun   bed   boy   ball   girl   tree

Choose one of these words to complete each of the sentences.

 A little __girl__ put on her dress.

 The _____ was hot.

I get into my _____ to go to sleep.

 I can see a bird's nest in the _____ .

Dad kicked the _____ .

 The _____ put on his football boots.

Note for parent: This activity helps children to read and understand key words.

Making sentences

These sentences are all muddled. Write them in the right order and then finish each one with a full stop **.** or a question mark **?**

is time What the

_____

chips I to like eat

_____

do go school When I to

_____

car going The was fast

_____

up Who the with went Jill hill

_____

on lap The likes sit to my cat

_____

How many capital letters can you count?_____

Note for parent: This activity gives practice with sorting words to make sense and using punctuation.

Alphabetical order

Look at the names and then write them in the register in the correct order. Remember the capital letters.

Alison

Imran

Jamilla

Class Register

Alison

Duncan

Meena

Wendy

Samuel

Wendy

Patrick

Note for parent: This activity helps children to practise using alphabetical order for a familiar situation.

Find your way

Read these instructions. Draw the correct way from the house to the school.

Start at **X**

Walk down the path and turn right out of the gate.

Turn right again past some trees.

Walk along the path to the traffic lights.

Cross the road when it is safe.

Turn right and then turn left into **School Road**.

Go past the fence and turn left through the school gate.

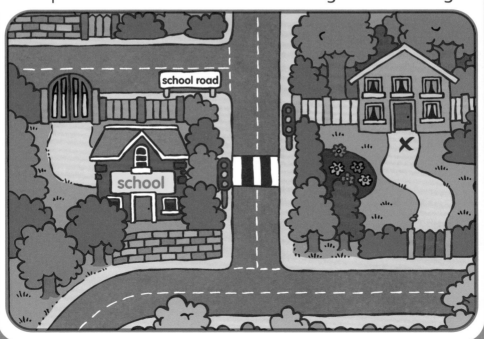

Note for parent: This activity helps children to read instructions and follow them.

Telephone numbers

Use this telephone directory to answer the
questions at the bottom of the page.

Mr Anderson	9802	Mr Mead	9980
Mr Caswell	9146	Miss Palmer	9544
Mrs Depster	9829	Mr Shah	9827
Miss Heelan	9026	Mrs Todd	9412
Ms Kamara	9530	Ms Walker	9361

What is Mr Shah's number? _____

What is Miss Heelan's number? _____

What is Mr Caswell's number? _____

What is Miss Palmer's number? _____

Whose number is 9361? _____

Whose number is 9802? _____

Whose number is 9412? _____

Whose number is 9829? _____

Do you know your own
telephone number at home? _____

Note for parent: This activity helps children to
learn how to use lists of numbers.

Animal dictionary

Match each word to the correct meaning.
Draw a line to join them.

elephant

A large animal that can jump very well. It carries its young in a pouch. It comes from Australia.

kangaroo

A small animal with long arms and feet that it uses like hands. It lives in jungles.

monkey

A large animal with a long trunk and ivory tusks. It lives in Africa and Asia.

panda

An animal like a horse with black and white stripes. It lives in Africa.

zebra

A black and white animal like a bear. It lives in China.

Note for parent: This activity helps children to learn how to use a dictionary.

22

Reading an index

Use the index below to answer the questions at the bottom of the page.

Index

Apes	10	Kangaroos	20
Bears	8	Monkeys	6
Chimpanzees	14	Penguins	28
Crocodiles	22	Sharks	4
Dolphins	26	Turtles	12
Giraffes	18	Whales	16

Page 28 is about _____

Page 16 is about _____

Page 8 is about _____

Apes are on page _____

Sharks are on page _____

Kangaroos are on page _____

Giraffes are on page _____

Which page would you like to read? _____

Why? _____

Pictures and sounds

Write the first two letters.

Join two pictures that start in the same way.

Note for parent: This page gives children a chance to practise what they have learned.

24

Making lists

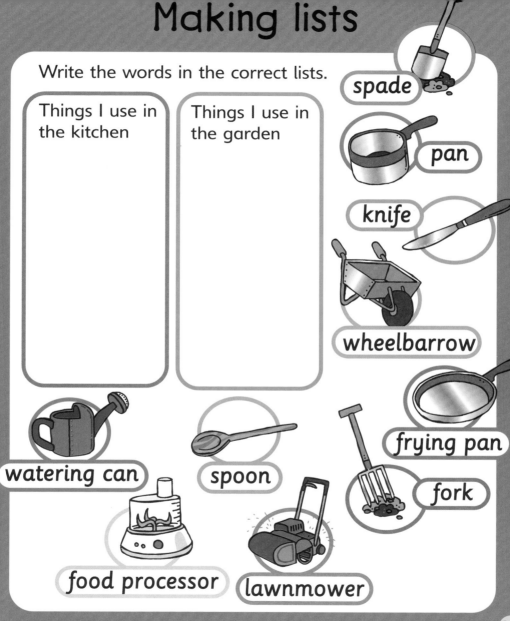

Write the words in the correct lists.

spade

Things I use in the kitchen	Things I use in the garden

pan

knife

wheelbarrow

watering can

spoon

frying pan

fork

food processor

lawnmower

Note for parent: This activity gives children practice with sorting things into lists.

25

Patterns in words

Make two more words by adding one letter.

b<u>all</u>   **_all**   **_all**

Write a sentence with each of the two words you have made.

1._____

2._____

Now do the same again.

m<u>an</u>   **_an**   **_an**

h<u>at</u>   **_at**   **_at**

1._____

2._____

1._____

2._____

Note for parent: This activity encourages
children to look for patterns in words.

26

Find the rhymes

Colour in blue the words that rhyme with **take**.
Colour in green the words that rhyme with **ball**.
Colour in red the words that rhyme with **shell**.
Colour in yellow the words that rhyme with **pin**.

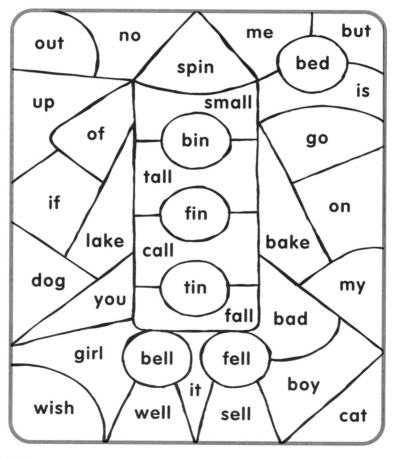

out · no · spin · me · but · bed · up · small · is · of · bin · go · tall · if · fin · on · lake · call · bake · dog · tin · my · you · fall · bad · girl · bell · fell · wish · well · it · sell · boy · cat

Note for parent: This activity helps children to
see patterns and to hear rhymes in words.

Counting to 5

Write the numbers. Join each picture to the right number. Join each word to the right number.

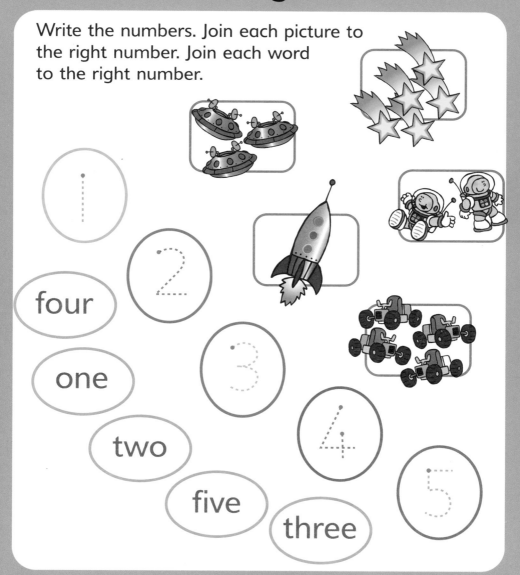

four

one

two

five

three

Note for parent: With this activity you will find out if your child can recognize the numbers 1 to 5 and count up to 5.

Counting to 10

Write the numbers. Join each word to the right number and picture.

Note for parent: With this activity you will find out if your child can recognize the numbers and count up to 10.

More counting

Count the spots on each dog.
Write the number in the box.

Join the frogs that have the
same number of spots.

 Note for parent: This activity gives practice in
using counting skills in different ways.

30

Starting to add

Write in the missing numbers.

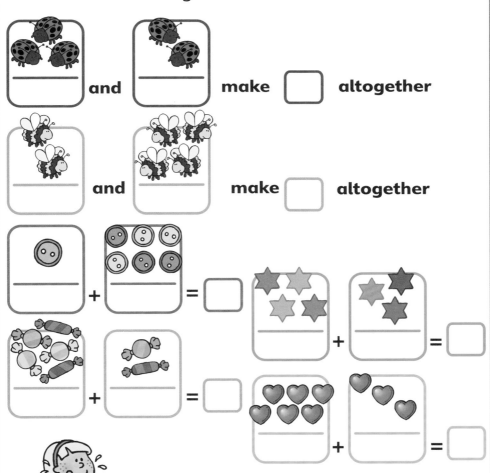

_____ and _____ make ☐ altogether

_____ and _____ make ☐ altogether

☐ + ☐ = ☐

☐ + ☐ = ☐

☐ + ☐ = ☐

☐ + ☐ = ☐

Note for parent: In this activity your child is adding pictures, rather than just numbers.

Starting to take away

Dino the Dinosaur eats 2 of everything he sees.
Cross out the pieces of food Dino eats.
Write how many are left after Dino has eaten.

☐ take away **2**

leaves ☐

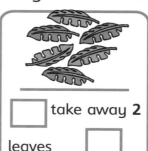

☐ take away **2**

leaves ☐

☐ take away **2**

leaves ☐

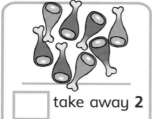

☐ take away **2**

leaves ☐

☐ take away **2**

leaves ☐

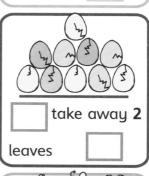

☐ take away **2**

leaves ☐

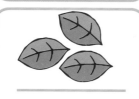

3 – 2 = ☐

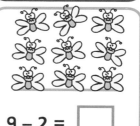

2 – 2 = ☐

9 – 2 = ☐

Note for parent: Taking away is the start to learning
about subtraction.

Looking at shapes

Some of these foods are whole and some have been cut up into pieces. Join each whole to a cut-up piece.

 Note for parent: This activity encourages your child to examine shapes closely.

Matching shapes

Colour the matching shapes.

 colour red

 colour green

 colour blue

 colour orange

Note for parent: This activity gives further
practice in examining shapes closely.

Solid shapes

Join each set of shapes to its name.

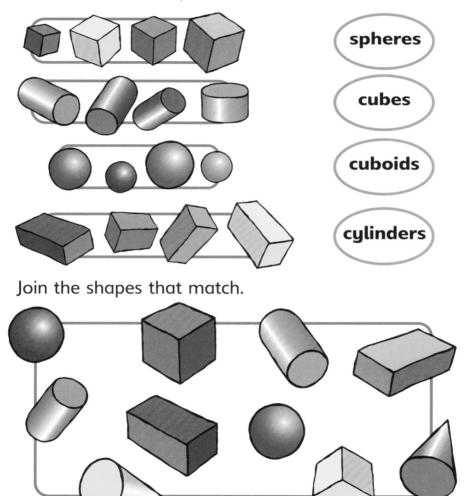

spheres

cubes

cuboids

cylinders

Join the shapes that match.

Note for parent: Your child will gradually learn the names of common shapes.

All about halves

Colour half of each shape.

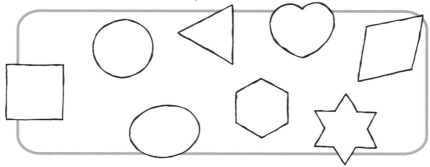

Draw the missing half of each shape.
Join the complete shape to its name.

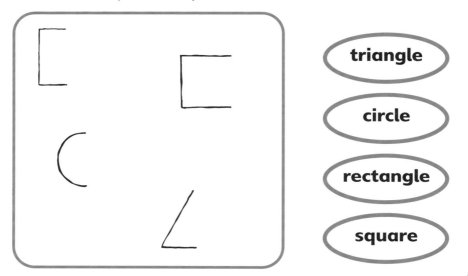

triangle

circle

rectangle

square

Note for parent: Learning about half and fair shares is important in mathematics.

More about halves

Colour half of the items in each container.

Some marbles are put into two bags.
Put a tick (✔) if the sharing is fair.
Put a cross (✘) if the sharing is not fair.

Note for parent: Learning about half and fair shares is important in mathematics.

Adding

Draw in the extra crayons.
Write the total number of crayons.

 1 add 4

1 + 4 =

 3 add 3

3 + 3 =

 4 add 6

4 + 6 =

There should be 10 cherries on each plate. Draw the missing cherries.

4 +   = 10

8 +   = 10

Note for parent: Your child may need to use the
number track on page 39 to complete these additions.

More adding

Use the number track to help you.
Write how many beads are on each necklace.

4 + 3 =

6 + 2 =

2 + 5 =

3 + 3 =

1 + 5 =

Join the scarves that have the same total.

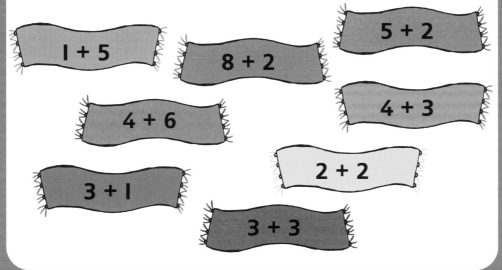

1 + 5

8 + 2

5 + 2

4 + 6

4 + 3

3 + 1

2 + 2

3 + 3

Subtracting

Cross off the animals to be taken away.
Write how many are left.

4 take away **2**

$4 - 2 =$

7 take away **3**

$7 - 3 =$

8 take away **5**

$8 - 5 =$

Only 3 rockets are needed. Cross off the rockets
that have to be taken away. Write the answer.

$5 - \quad = 3$

$7 - \quad = 3$

Note for parent: Your child may need to use the number track on
page 41 to complete these subtractions.

More subtracting

Use the number track to help you answer the subtractions.

$4 - 1 =$

$5 - 3 =$

$8 - 7 =$

$5 - 5 =$

$9 - 5 =$

$10 - 2 =$

Join the stars that have the same answer.

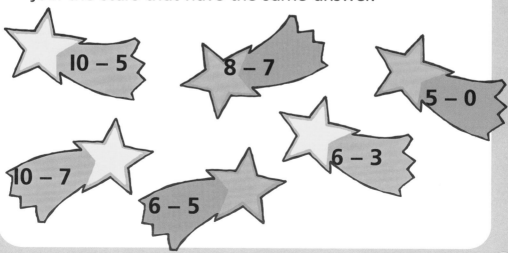

$10 - 5$

$8 - 7$

$5 - 0$

$10 - 7$

$6 - 3$

$6 - 5$

Flat shapes

Cross the odd one out in each ring.

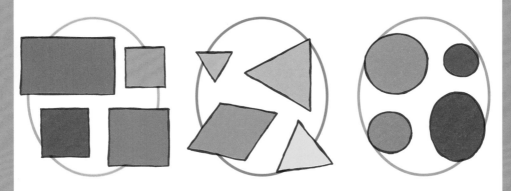

Tick all the shapes that are the same in each row.

 Note for parent: This activity gives practice in recognizing shapes.

42

Sets and pairs

Join each set of shapes to its name.

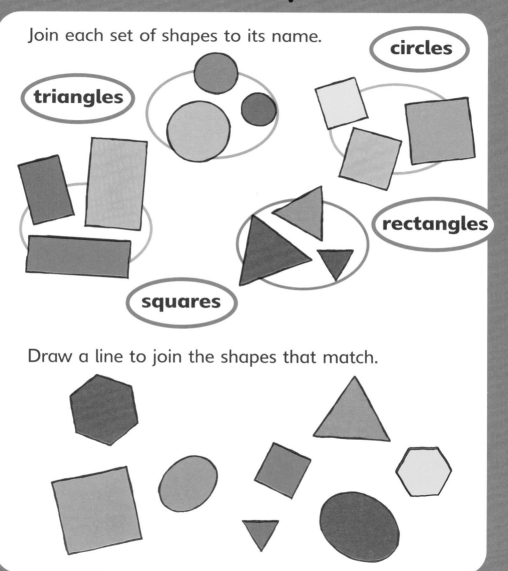

circles

triangles

rectangles

squares

Draw a line to join the shapes that match.

Note for parent: Gradually your child should learn the names of common shapes.

Time

Write in the missing numbers on the clock.

Write the times under each clock.

____ o'clock

____ o'clock

____ o'clock

Note for parent: This activity will help your child to start telling the time.

Time again

Look at the times. Draw in the missing hands.

half-past 3

half-past 8

half-past 12

Write the times under each clock.

half-past _____

half-past _____

half-past _____

Note for parent: This activity gives practice in recognizing simple times.

Measuring

Draw a longer worm.

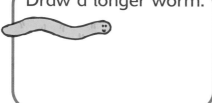

Draw a bigger flower.

Draw a taller rocket.

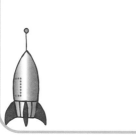

Draw a shorter lamp post.

Join up the pictures in order of size.
Start with the smallest.

Note for parent: In this activity your child is learning to compare measurements.

Counting to 20

Write in the missing numbers.

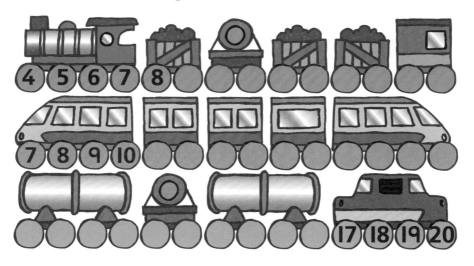

Join each word to a number.

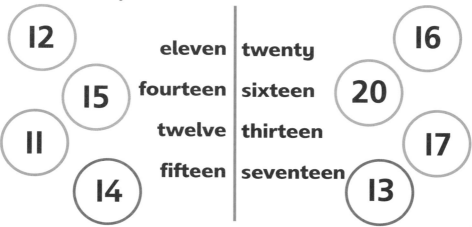

12 15 11 14

eleven fourteen twelve fifteen

twenty sixteen thirteen seventeen

16 20 17 13

Note for parent: This activity gives your child practice in counting to 20, and in recognizing numbers and words.

Number words

Colour the balloons.

1 = red   2 = purple   3 = yellow   4 = blue
5 = green   6 = red   7 = purple
8 = yellow   9 = blue   10 = green

one

two

three

four

five

six

seven

eight

nine

ten

Note for parent: Learning to recognize written numbers is an important skill.

48

Word endings

Look at the first picture in each row.
Draw a ring round two pictures in each row that have the same ending as the first.

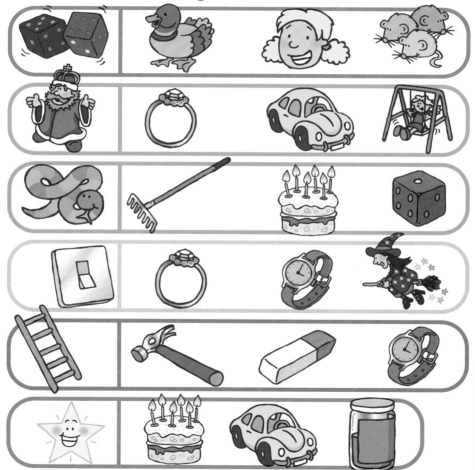

Note for parent: This activity encourages children to
listen carefully to word endings.

49

All about nouns

Words that name people, animals, things and places are called **nouns**. Read these sentences and draw a line under each noun.

The boy is reading a book.

The girl is looking at the television.

The dog is playing with a ball.

The man is cutting the grass.

Find another noun in each picture and write it below.

_____   _____

_____   _____

Note for parent: This activity helps children to learn about nouns.

Adjectives

An **adjective** tells you more about someone or something.
Choose an adjective to fill in the missing words in the sentences below.

cold   **windy**   **blue**
happy   **small**   **fresh**

1. A ladybird is very _____ .

2. The leaves fell off the tree because it was
   _____ .

3. The sun was shining and the sky
   was _____ .

4. Dad had just picked the flowers so they
   were _____ .

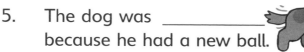 

5. The dog was _____
   because he had a new ball.

6. It was _____ in the garden
   and there was ice on the pond.

Note for parent: This activity helps children to
understand what an adjective is.

In the dictionary

A **dictionary** tells you how to spell words. The words on this page have incorrect spellings. Look them up in a dictionary and write them correctly.

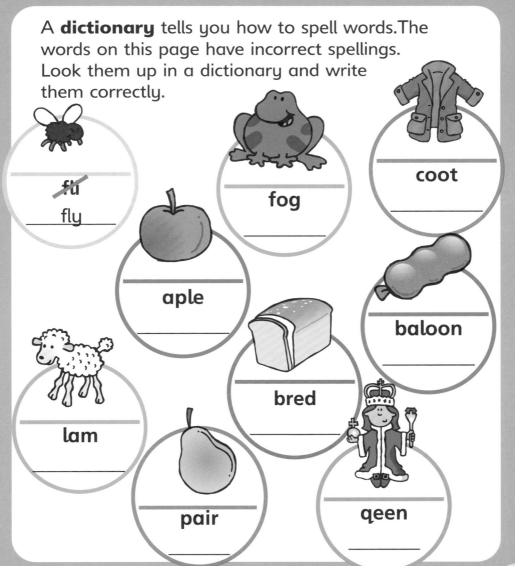

flu ~~flu~~
fly

fog

coot

aple

baloon

lam

bred

pair

qeen

Note for parent: This activity gives practice in learning to use a dictionary.

Dictionary skills

A dictionary also tells you what words mean.
This is called a **definition**. Draw a line to join each
word to the correct definition.

	boy	A creature you read about in fairy tales.
	hutch	A black-and-white bird that cannot fly.
	monster	A tool that has sharp metal teeth.
	saw	A male child.
	penguin	A pet rabbit's home.

Now draw a picture for each word to
make your own picture dictionary.

Note for parent: This activity gives practice in using definitions.

Using verbs

A **verb** tells you what someone or something is doing. Tick the verb in each box.

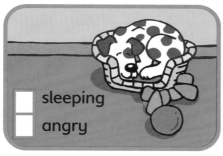

- [ ] sleeping
- [ ] angry

- [ ] happy
- [ ] licking

- [ ] running
- [ ] cold

- [ ] windy
- [ ] climbing

- [ ] dirty
- [ ] swimming

- [ ] flying
- [ ] fresh

What are you doing now? _____

 Note for parent: This activity helps children to understand verbs.

54

Months of the year

Class 2 have made a chart to show when the children have their birthdays.

January	February	March	April
Solomon	Brian	Alison	Imran
Duncan	Jamilla		
May	**June**	**July**	**August**
Ellen	Mark	Dale	Pat
Paul	Lisa	Kerry	Polly
Zara	Ahmed		Frank
Ben			
September	**October**	**November**	**December**
	Meena	Amy	Brendan
	Wendy		Connor
			Sally
			Gail

1. When is Amy's birthday? _____

2. When is Solomon's birthday? _____

3. Which month has no birthday?_____

4. Which months have the most birthdays?

_____

When is your birthday?_____

Note for parent: This activity helps children to learn the months of the year.

Fill in the gaps

Use these letters to fill in the gaps: **ai** (nail) or **ea** (meat). Read the words when you have made them.

l_ _f

sn_ _ l

p_ _ch

s_ _l

s_ _ _t

Now use these letters to fill the gaps: **oa** (goat) or **ou** (house).

cl_ _d

m_ _ _se

c_ _t

r_ _ _d

tr_ _ _sers

Note for parent: These sounds are not easy. Read the words in brackets to help your child.

Descriptions

Look at the picture. Write a short sentence saying what everyone is doing. Try to include a noun, a verb and an adjective in your sentences.

Note for parent: This activity helps children learn how to describe people using proper sentences.

Compound words

You make a compound word by joining two smaller words together.

 horse + **shoe** = **horseshoe**

Now try to make compound words from the words below:

1 star + fish = _____

2 water + fall = _____

3 home + work = _____

4 play + time = _____

5 tooth + brush = _____

Note for parent: This activity gives practice in making compound words.

Making new words

You can make new words by changing some of the letters in a word.

change the **p** in **park** to **m** → **mark**
change the **p** in **park** to **sh** → **shark**

Now try to make these new words.

1. Change the **b** in **bear** to **p** → _____

to **w** → _____

2. Change the **j** in **jaw** to **cl** → _____

to **str** → _____

3. Change the **br** in **brown** to **cl** → _____

to **cr** → _____

4. Change the **fl** in **flight** to **br** → _____

to **kn**→ _____

Note for parent: This activity helps children to understand the composition of words.

Missing letters

Sometimes when we talk to people
we do not say every word.

I am = I'm   It is = It's

Join the words on the left side of
the page to the smaller words on the right.

is not	I'd
cannot	won't
I would	isn't
I am	I'm
will not	you've
you have	can't

Write these sentences again using smaller words
instead of the underlined words:

<u>I would</u> like to see you but <u>I am</u> ill. <u>I cannot</u> go out
but <u>I would</u> like to see you if you have time and it
<u>is not</u> too far for you to come.

_____

_____

_____

Note for parent: Try to explain how an apostrophe
is always used in these shortened versions.

60

Writing postcards

Write a postcard to a relative (for example your granny, a cousin, an uncle) telling them about your school.

Dear _____

Draw a picture that might be on the other side of the postcard, or cut out a picture and stick it here.

Reading instructions

Read the instructions and then draw on the pictures.

1. Draw a hat on the first clown.

2. Draw long shoes on the second clown.

3. Draw spots on the trousers of the third clown.

4. Draw curly hair on the third clown.

5. Draw a smile on the face of the first clown.

Note for parent: This activity gives practice in following instructions.

Silly or sensible?

Some of these sentences are silly, and some are sensible. Read each one and then write the word **silly** or **sensible** beside it.

1. A library is a place to borrow babies. _____

2. Clocks help us to tell the time. _____

3. All boys have black hair. _____

4. Teachers like to teach bananas. _____

5. Cats have baby puppies. _____

6. There are lots of animals at the zoo. _____

Now write two sentences yourself:

A silly sentence: _____

_____

A sensible sentence: _____

_____

Note for parent: In this activity children can practise responding to different sentences.

Odd one out

Cross out the word that does not belong in each row.

1. square   triangle   circle   shape   rectangle
2. paint   red   orange   blue   green
3. sheep   horse   pig   cow   lion
4. bus   car   man   lorry   van

Now put the words in the correct group.

Shapes   Farm animals   Vehicles   Colours

_____   _____   _____   _____

_____   _____   _____   _____

_____   _____   _____   _____

_____   _____   _____   _____

Note for parent: This activity helps children to understand categories of words.

64

Opposites

An **antonym** is a word that has the opposite meaning to another word.

big   **small**   **happy**   **sad**

Read the words in the box.

pull	**near**	**dry**	**cold**	**full**
hard	**long**	**light**	**last**	**day**

Use the words in the box to write the antonym of each word in this list.

1. wet _____
2. soft _____
3. first _____
4. far _____
5. empty _____

6. hot _____
7. night _____
8. push _____
9. short _____
10. heavy _____

Note for parent: This activity helps children to understand and use opposites.

Finish the sentences

Draw a line to join the beginning of each sentence to the correct ending.

1. The dog barked   into the air.

2. The horse galloped   a big web.

3. The frog jumped   on the wall.

4. The birds flew   at the burglar.

5. The spider spun   across the field.

6. The cat slept   out of the pond.

Now finish these sentences.

The dolphin jumped _____ .

The kangaroo hopped _____ .

 Note for parent: This activity helps with comprehension and making choices.

Word search

Look for these words in the grid below.

nouns	verbs	adjectives
dog	runs	fast
tree	grows	tall
mouse	squeaks	soft

a	e	m	c	i	g	r	t	h	j
s	r	l	c	b	t	a	l	q	k
d	o	g	s	g	r	o	w	s	z
f	k	f	m	u	e	s	b	g	s
d	g	s	t	t	e	q	n	q	u
r	u	n	s	u	f	u	d	m	p
p	x	a	l	j	y	e	u	o	n
w	f	l	o	o	v	a	l	u	t
y	a	z	e	v	n	k	y	s	b
t	h	x	a	e	c	s	w	e	d

Now find all the letters of the alphabet and colour them red. There are 26 to find.

Note for parent: This activity helps children to recognize nouns, verbs and adjectives.

A puzzle page

Make as many words as you can from the letters.

p	o	r
l	e	t
i	s	a
r	e	m

You can move in any direction but do not jump a square.

_____   _____

_____   _____

_____   _____

_____   _____

How many words did you find?

Change one letter to make a new word.

man   _____   You cook food in this.

coat   _____   You go on water in this.

robber _____   You rub out with this.

card   _____   A horse can pull this.

fork   _____   Soldiers live in this.

wolf   _____   This is a sport.

Note for parent: These activities are just for fun, but they are not easy.

Adding to 12

Write the totals.

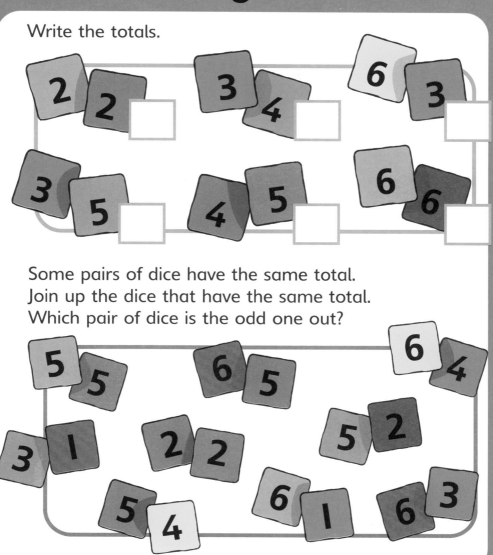

Some pairs of dice have the same total.
Join up the dice that have the same total.
Which pair of dice is the odd one out?

Note for parent: Encourage your child to work out
the totals quickly and not rely on using fingers.

More adding to 12

Write the missing number in each box.

Here is a pair of number adding machines.
Write in the missing numbers.

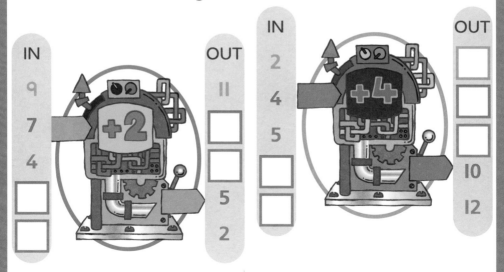

Note for parent: Encourage your child to work out
the totals quickly and not rely on using fingers.

Subtracting to 12

Write the answers at the end of the trail.

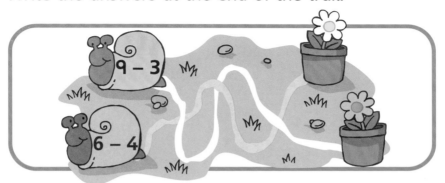

Each child only catches fish to match the number on his or her shirt. Join up each child to the correct fish. Colour the fish that no one catches.

Note for parent: Encourage children to work the answers out quickly and not rely on their fingers.

Number mazes

Write the missing numbers.

Note for parent: This activity gives further practice
in subtracting up to 12.

72

Sums up to 12

Whizzy Wendy has made some numbers disappear.
Write in the missing numbers.

3 + ⭐ = 7
⭐ − 5 = 2

4 + ⭐ = 8
12 − ⭐ = 6

7 + ⭐ = 9
⭐ − 6 = 0

6 + ⭐ = 8
11 − ⭐ = 8

Write in the missing sign + or −.

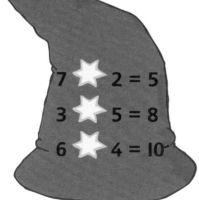

7 ⭐ 2 = 5

3 ⭐ 5 = 8

6 ⭐ 4 = 10

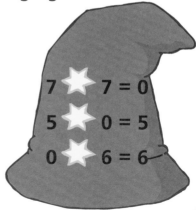

7 ⭐ 7 = 0

5 ⭐ 0 = 5

0 ⭐ 6 = 6

Note for parent: Encourage children to avoid using their fingers to work out these answers.

More sums up to 12

Join each broomstick to a magic star.
Colour red the star that has no broomstick.
Colour blue the star that has two broomsticks.

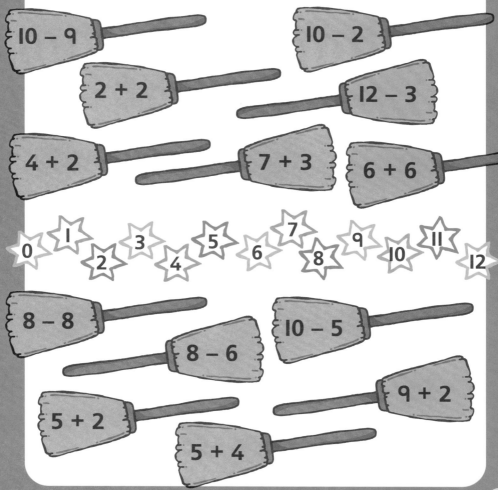

Note for parent: Encourage children to avoid using
their fingers to work out these answers.

Numbers to 100

Join each number to its word.

(10) (20) (30) (40) (50) (60) (70) (80) (90) (100)

forty   one hundred   thirty   eighty

sixty   ten   fifty

twenty   ninety   seventy

Write which number comes after each of these.
Colour each even number.

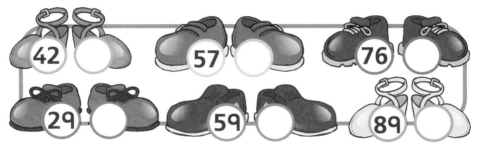

42   57   76

29   59   89

Write which number comes before each of these.
Colour each odd number.

46   64   85

30   50   70

Note for parent: This activity develops ideas of
numbers up to 100, including odd and even numbers.

Shapes

Write the missing numbers.

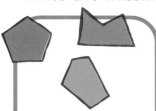 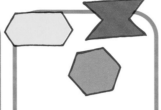 

Pentagons have ☐ sides.

Hexagons have ☐ sides.

Octagons have ☐ sides.

Join each shape to its name.

(**triangle**) (**pentagon**) (**hexagon**) (**octagon**)

Put a cross on the odd one out in each box.

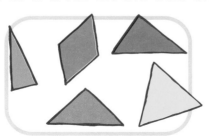 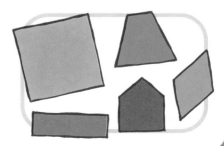

Note for parent: It is useful to know the names of 2-D and 3-D shapes.

More shapes

These shapes are joined to the correct names.

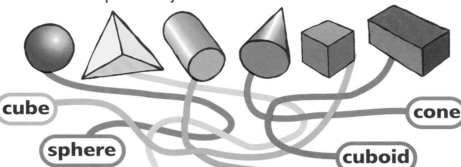

Join the shapes to their names.

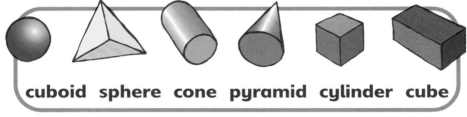

cuboid sphere cone pyramid cylinder cube

Put a cross on the odd one out in each box.

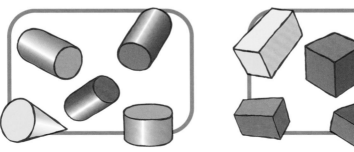

Note for parent: It is useful to know the names of 2-D and 3-D shapes.

Adding to 20

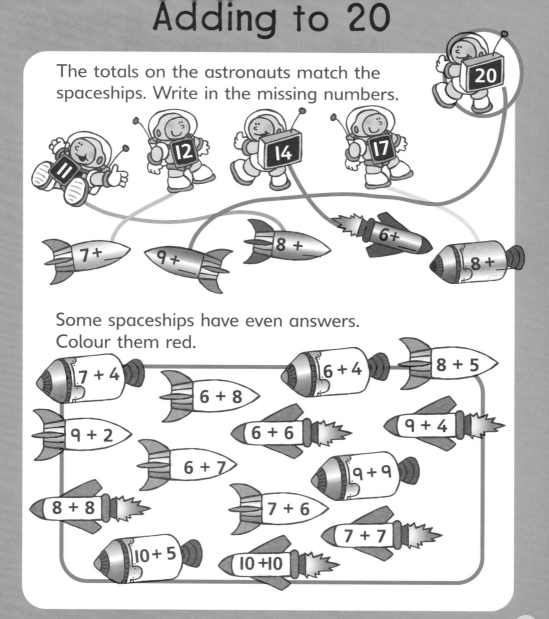

The totals on the astronauts match the spaceships. Write in the missing numbers.

20

11   12   14   17

7 + _
9 + _
8 + _
6 + _
8 + _

Some spaceships have even answers.
Colour them red.

7 + 4   6 + 4   8 + 5
6 + 8
9 + 2   6 + 6   9 + 4
6 + 7   9 + 9
8 + 8   7 + 6   7 + 7
10 + 5   10 + 10

Note for parent: This activity gives more practice in adding numbers up to 20.

Subtracting to 20

Join each mother hen to a chick.

One egg in each basket has a different answer.
Colour the eggs that are the odd ones out.

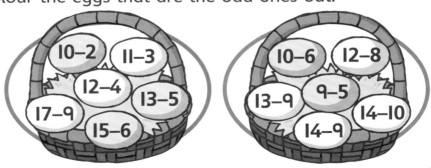

 Note for parent: If children cannot work out the answers in their head, encourage them to use the number line.

Mystery numbers

Write each answer in words. Discover the mystery number in the shaded squares.

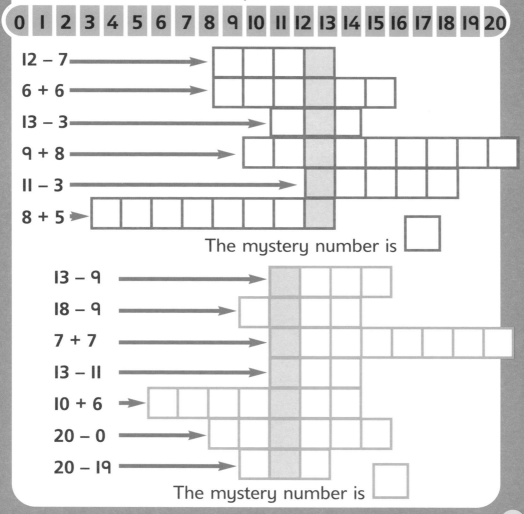

0 1 2 3 4 5 6 7 8 9 10 11 12 13 14 15 16 17 18 19 20

12 – 7

6 + 6

13 – 3

9 + 8

11 – 3

8 + 5

The mystery number is

13 – 9

18 – 9

7 + 7

13 – 11

10 + 6

20 – 0

20 – 19

The mystery number is

Note for parent: This activity gives more practice with addition and with number words.

Patterns

Complete the missing half of each picture.

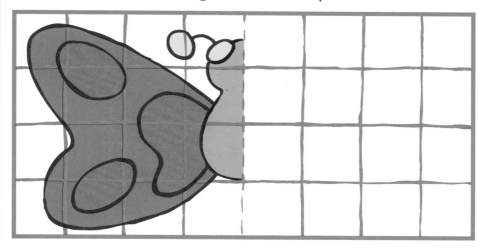

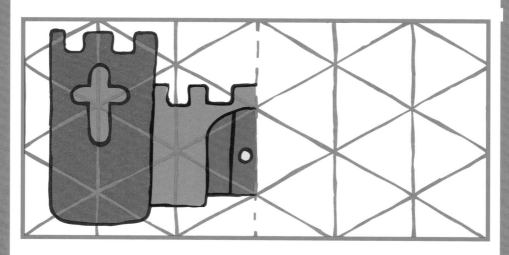

Note for parent: Ideas of pattern and symmetry are
important in understanding about shape.

More patterns

Colour each knight's shield to make a pattern.
Each pattern must be different.

Continue each pattern.

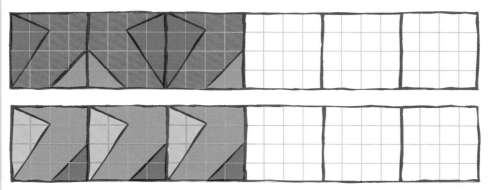

Tens and ones

Write the missing numbers using tens and ones.

15 = 10 + ☐   31 = 30 + ☐   64 = 60 + ☐

16 = 10 + ☐   39 = 30 + ☐   73 = 70 + ☐

19 = 10 + ☐   42 = 40 + ☐   85 = 80 + ☐

12 = ☐ + 2   36 = ☐ + 6   71 = ☐ + 1

25 = ☐ + 5   47 = ☐ + 7   89 = ☐ + 9

28 = ☐ + 8   57 = ☐ + 7   92 = ☐ + 2

13 = ☐ + ☐   43 = ☐ + ☐   62 = ☐ + ☐

26 = ☐ + ☐   48 = ☐ + ☐   75 = ☐ + ☐

Tick the smaller number in each pair.

Note for parent: This shows how large numbers are built up using tens and ones.

Words and numbers

Write the correct number on each child.

fifty-six   thirty-one   forty-five   sixty-four   seventy-three   twenty-six

Add 1 to each number.

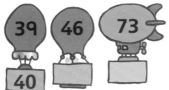

39   46   73

40

Subtract 1 from each number.

50   44   68

Add 10 to each number.

34   51   69

Subtract 10 from each number.

28   37   52

Note for parent: This activity gives further practice in working with large numbers.

Telling the time

Write the missing numbers on the clock face.

Make the clock show 7 o'clock.

Make each of these clocks and watches show 4 o'clock.

Make each of these clocks and watches show half-past two.

Note for parent: Telling the time on all kinds of clocks and watches is important.

More telling the time

One hour passes on each clock. Write the new times.

Join the clocks that say the same time.

Draw in the missing minute hand on each clock.

5:45   9:15   6:30   4:15

Note for parent: Telling the time on all kinds of clocks and watches is important.

86

Twos and tens

Write the missing numbers in the twos pattern.

| 2 | 4 | 6 | | | | | | | |

Write the hidden number next to each wheel.

x 2 = 6   x 2 = 10   x 2 = 16

2 x = 20   2 x = 4   2 x = 14

x 2 = 2   x 2 = 18   x 2 = 12

Write the missing numbers in the tens pattern.

| 10 | 20 | 30 | | | | | | | |

Write the hidden number next to each wheel.

x 10 = 30   x 10 = 60   x 10 = 20

10 x = 40   10 x = 90   10 x = 100

x 10 = 80   x 10 = 10

Note for parent: This is an early start to learning multiplication tables.

Fives, twos and tens

Write the missing numbers on the fives pattern.

5 10 15

Write the hidden number beside each leaf.

 x 5 = 5   x 5 = 15   x 5 = 45

5 x =25   5 x =30   5 x =10

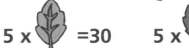 x 5 = 40   x 5 = 20   x 5 = 35

Write how many fives are in each group.

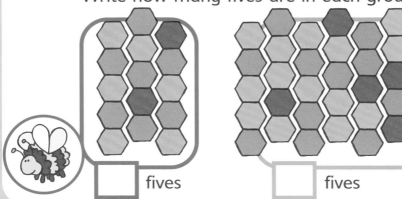

☐ fives   ☐ fives

Note for parent: Your child can start learning the 2x, 5x and 10x tables.

More fives, twos and tens

Write in the answers to these tables.

2 x 1 = ☐	5 x 1 = ☐	10 x 1 = ☐
2 x 2 = ☐	5 x 2 = ☐	10 x 2 = ☐
2 x 3 = ☐	5 x 3 = ☐	10 x 3 = ☐
2 x 4 = ☐	5 x 4 = ☐	10 x 4 = ☐
2 x 5 = ☐	5 x 5 = ☐	10 x 5 = ☐
2 x 6 = ☐	5 x 6 = ☐	10 x 6 = ☐
2 x 7 = ☐	5 x 7 = ☐	10 x 7 = ☐
2 x 8 = ☐	5 x 8 = ☐	10 x 8 = ☐
2 x 9 = ☐	5 x 9 = ☐	10 x 9 = ☐
2 x 10= ☐	5 x 10= ☐	10 x 10= ☐

Work out the answers. Join each saucer to a cup.

5 x 4   10 x 4   2 x 10   10 x 3   5 x 8

5 x 6   5 x 10   2 x 5   10 x 5   10 x 1

10   20   30   40   50

Note for parent: Your child can start learning the 2x, 5x and 10x tables.

89

Sharing

Join the balls to the clowns.
Each clown must have the same number of balls.

 balls for each clown

 balls for each clown

 balls for each clown

 Note for parent: This activity is an introduction to division.

More sharing

Write how many twos are in each tree.

[ ] twos

[ ] twos

Write how many threes are on each pond.

[ ] threes

[ ] threes

Write how many fours are in each bag.

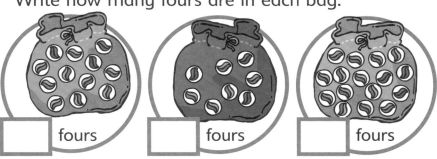

[ ] fours   [ ] fours   [ ] fours

Note for parent: This activity is an introduction to division.

Answers

Page 6
dog, fox, log;
hat, bat, fan;
bell, web, peg;
sum, jug, bus;
six, pig, lips.

Page 7
b<u>u</u>s, p<u>i</u>g, m<u>a</u>n, s<u>o</u>ck, r<u>e</u>d, cr<u>a</u>b, j<u>e</u>t, d<u>u</u>ck, f<u>i</u>sh.

Page 8
Row 1: book; row 2: tree;
row 3: cat; row 4: house;
row 5: bicycle.

Page 9
The teacher is under the table. ✗
A girl is reading a book. ✓
A boy is painting the door. ✗
The teacher is looking at the children. ✓
A cat is reading a book. ✗
A boy has got a brush. ✓
The hamster is on its cage. ✗

Page 11
<u>c</u>lock, <u>b</u>ridge, <u>c</u>rown, <u>b</u>lack;
<u>g</u>reen, <u>p</u>lug, <u>d</u>rill, <u>f</u>lag.

Page 12
cl – clown, dr – drum, sn – snail,
bl – blue, gr – grapes,
sp – spider, st – star, sw – swan.

Page 13
Everyone fell over and the turnip came out. **D**
The farmer saw an enormous turnip. **A**

Everyone tried to pull up the turnip. **C**
The farmer tried to pull up the turnip. **B**

Page 15
<u>b</u>all, <u>d</u>og, <u>c</u>at; bcd.
<u>h</u>ouse, <u>f</u>ish, <u>g</u>irl; fgh.
<u>l</u>adybird, <u>m</u>oon, <u>k</u>ey; klm.
<u>r</u>abbit, <u>q</u>ueen, <u>p</u>arachute; pqr.
<u>u</u>mbrella, <u>s</u>eesaw, <u>t</u>elevision; stu.

Page 16
or – fork, us – bus, an – man,
all – ball, am – lamb, in – twins,
at – bat.

Page 17
A little <u>girl</u> put on her dress.
The <u>sun</u> was hot.
I get into my <u>bed</u> to go to sleep.
I can see a bird's nest in the <u>tree</u>.
Dad kicked the <u>ball</u>.
A little <u>boy</u> put on his football boots.

Page 18
What is the time?
I like to eat chips.
When do I go to school?
The car was going fast.
Who went up the hill with Jill?
The cat likes to sit on my lap.

There are 8 capital letters.

Page 19
Alison, Duncan, Imran, Jamilla, Meena, Patrick, Samuel, Wendy.

Page 21
9827, 9026, 9146, 9544.
Ms Walker
Mr Anderson
Mrs Todd
Mrs Depster

Page 22
elephant:
A large animal with a long trunk and ivory tusks. It lives in Africa and Asia.

kangaroo:
A large animal that can jump very well. It carries its young in a pouch. It comes from Australia.

monkey:
A small animal with long arms and feet that it uses like hands. It lives in jungles.

panda:
A black and white animal like a bear. It lives in China.

zebra:
An animal like a horse with black and white stripes. It lives in Africa.

Page 23
penguins, whales, bears.
10, 4, 20, 18.

Answers

Page 24

cl, br, cr, bl;
dr, gr, pl, fl.

spider – spade
snake – snail
swan – swing
star – stool

Page 25

Kitchen: pan / knife / frying pan
/ spoon / food processor.
Garden: spade / wheelbarrow /
watering can / fork /
lawnmower.

Page 30

clockwise from top left: 8 spots,
10 spots, 6 spots, 4 spots, 7 spots,
9 spots.

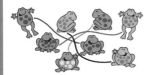

Page 31

3 and 2 make 5 altogether,
2 and 4 make 6 altogether.
buttons: 1 + 6 = 7;
stars: 4 + 3 = 7;
sweets: 5 + 2 = 7;
hearts: 6 + 3 = 9.

Page 32

row 1: 4 take away 2 leaves 2;
6 take away 2 leaves 4;
5 take away 2 leaves 3.
row 2: 8 take away 2 leaves 6;
7 take away 2 leaves 5;
10 take away 2 leaves 8.
row 3: 3 – 2 = 1, 2 – 2 = 0,
9 – 2 = 7.

Page 33

Page 35

row 1 are cubes; row 2 are
cylinders; row 3 are spheres;
row 4 are cuboids.

Page 36

△ triangle, ○ circle,

▭ rectangle, ▢ square.

Page 37

red bags = ✘
yellow bags = ✔

Page 38

1 + 4 = 5, 3 + 3 = 6, 4 + 6 = 10.
4 + 6 = 10, 8 + 2 = 10.

Page 39

4 + 3 = 7, 6 + 2 = 8, 2 + 5 = 7,
3 + 3 = 6, 1 + 5 = 6.

total of 4: red and yellow scarves;
total of 6: orange and dark-blue
scarves; total of 7: pink and bright-
blue scarves; total of 10: green and
purple scarves.

Page 40

4 – 2 = 2, 7 – 3 = 4, 8 – 5 = 3,
5 – 2 = 3, 7 – 4 = 3.

Page 41

4 – 1 = 3, 5 – 3 = 2, 8 – 7 = 1,
5 – 5 = 0, 9 – 5 = 4, 10 – 2 = 8.
10 – 5 and 5 – 0;
8 – 7 and 6 – 5;
10 – 7 and 6 – 3.

Page 42

Page 43

rectangles, triangles, circles, squares

Page 44

11 o'clock, 8 o'clock, 5 o'clock.

Page 45

From left to right: half-past 4,
half-past 10, half-past 7.

Answers

Page 46

Page 47

Top train: 9, 10, 11, 12, 13, 14, 15, 16, 17. Middle train: 11, 12, 13, 14, 15, 16, 17, 18, 19, 20. Bottom train: 7, 8, 9, 10, 11, 12, 13, 14, 15, 16.

eleven–11, fourteen–14, twelve–12, fifteen–15, twenty–20, sixteen–16, thirteen–13, seventeen–17.

Page 49

Page 50

1. The <u>boy</u> is reading a <u>book</u>.
2. The <u>girl</u> is looking at the <u>television</u>.
3. The <u>dog</u> is playing with a <u>ball</u>.
4. The <u>man</u> is cutting the <u>grass</u>.

Some of the nouns are:
1. sofa, lamp, mug, shoes.
2. slippers, book, chair.
3. tree, house, grass.
4. lawnmower, flowers, boots, hat.

Page 51

1. A ladybird is very <u>small</u>.
2. The leaves fell off the tree because it was <u>windy</u>.
3. The sun was shining and the sky was <u>blue</u>. 4. Dad had just picked the flowers so they were <u>fresh</u>. 5. The dog was <u>happy</u> because he had a new ball.
6. It was <u>cold</u> in the garden and there was ice on the pond.

Page 52

fog = frog; coot = coat;
aple = apple; lam = lamb;
bred = bread;
baloon = balloon;
pair = pear; qeen = queen

Page 53

boy = A male child.
hutch = A pet rabbit's home.
monster = A creature you read about in fairy tales.
saw = A tool that has sharp metal teeth.
penguin = A black-and-white bird that cannot fly.

Page 54

top: sleeping, licking.
middle: running, climbing.
bottom: swimming, flying.

Page 55

1. November. 2. January.
3. September.
4. May and December.

Page 56

leaf, snail, peach, seal, seat.
cloud, mouse, coat, road, trousers.

Page 57

Possible answers are:
Dad is playing with a red ball.
The baby is eating a big ice cream.
The brown dog is chasing the cat.
Mum is feeding the hungry ducks.

Page 58

starfish, waterfall, homework, playtime, toothbrush.

Page 59

bear – pear – wear;
jaw – claw – straw;
brown – clown – crown;
flight – bright – knight.

Page 60

is not = isn't; cannot = can't;
I would = I'd; I am = I'm;
will not = won't;
you have = you've.

I'd like to see you but I'm ill. I can't go out but I'd like to see you if you have time and it's not too far for you to come.

Answers

Page 63
1. silly; 2. sensible; 3. silly;
4. silly; 5. silly; 6. sensible.

Page 64
1. shape; 2. paint;
3. lion; 4. man.
Shapes = square, triangle, circle, rectangle. Farm animals = sheep, horse, pig, cow.
Vehicles = bus, car, lorry, van.
Colours = red, orange, blue, green.

Page 65
1. wet–dry; 2. soft–hard;
3. first–last; 4. far–near;
5. empty–full; 6. hot–cold;
7. night–day; 8. push–pull;
9. short–long; 10. heavy–light.

Page 66
1. The dog barked at the burglar. 2. The horse galloped across the field. 3. The frog jumped out of the pond.
4. The birds flew into the air.
5. The spider spun a big web.
6. The cat slept on the wall.

Page 67

a	e	m	c	i	g	r	t	h	j
s	r	l	c	b	t	a	l	q	k
d	o	g	s	g	r	o	w	s	z
f	k	f	m	u	e	s	b	g	s
d	g	s	t	e	q	n	q	u	
r	u	n	s	u	f	u	d	m	p
p	x	a	l	j	y	e	u	o	n
w	l	o	o	v	a	l	u	t	
y	a	z	e	v	n	k	y	s	b
t	h	x	a	e	c	s	w	e	d

Page 68
Some of the words you can make are: or, let, is, as, pea, at, mat, me.
man/pan; coat/boat; robber/rubber; card/cart; fork/fort; wolf/golf.

Page 69
2+2=4, 3+4=7, 6+3=9,
3+5=8, 4+5 =9, 6+6=12.
5+5 and 6+4 (=10),
3+1 and 2+2 (=4),
5+2 and 6+1 (=7),
5+4 and 6+3 (=9).
Odd one out is 6+5.

Page 70
3+5=8, 2+8=10, 5+7=12,
7+4=11, 4+5=9. +2 machine:
IN: 3, 0; OUT: 9, 6. +4 machine:
IN: 6, 8; OUT: 6, 8, 9.

Page 71
9–3=6, 6–4=2. 9-6=3, 5-3=2,
12–7=5, 12–6=6, 10–6=4.
No-one catches the fish 11–2.

Page 72
11–3=8, 10–3=7, 6–3=3,
5–3=2.

7–5=2, 12–5=7, 5–5=0,
9–5=4.

Page 73
3+4=7, 7–5=2, 4+4=8,
12–6=6, 7+2=9, 6–6=0,
6+2=8, 11–3=8.
7–2=5, 3+5=8, 6+4=10,
7–7=0, 5+ or –0 =5, 0+6=6.

Page 74
10–9=1, 10–2=8, 2+2=4,
12–3=9, 4+2=6, 7+3=10,
6+6=12.

8–8=0,10–5=5, 8–6=2,
5+2=7, 9+2=11, 5+4=9.

The 3 star has no broomstick.
The 9 star has two broomsticks
(12–3=9, 5+4=9).

Page 75
10–ten, 20–twenty, 30–thirty,
40–forty, 50–fifty, 60–sixty,
70–seventy, 80–eighty,
90–ninety, 100–one hundred.
43, 58, 77, 30, 60, 90. Even numbers are: 42, 58, 76, 30, 60, 90.
45, 63, 84, 29, 49, 69.
Odd numbers are: 45, 63, 85, 29, 49, 69.

Page 76
Pentagons have 5 sides.
Hexagons have 6 sides.
Octagons have 8 sides.

Page 77

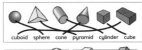
cuboid sphere cone pyramid cylinder cube

Answers

Page 78
7+5=12, 9+11=20, 8+3=11, 6+8=14, 8+9=17.
Red spaceships are: 6+8, 6+4, 6+6, 9+9, 8+8, 7+7, 10+10.

Page 79
12−9=3, 16-5=11, 13-8=5, 14-7=7, 15-6=9, 17-9=8, 12-8=4, 15-9=6, 19-9=10, 11-9=2.
The eggs 15−6 and 14−9 are the odd ones out.

Page 80
Mystery numbers are 11 and 15.

Page 81

Page 82

Page 83
Missing numbers are (from left to right): Top: 5, 1, 4; 6, 9, 3; 9, 2, 5. Middle:10, 30,70; 20, 40, 80; 20, 50, 90.
Bottom: 13=10+3, 43=40+3, 62=60+2, 26=20+6, 48=40+8, 75=70+5.

Page 84

47, 74; 49, 43, 67; 44, 61, 79; 18, 27, 42.

Page 85

Page 86
6.00, 6.15, 6.30, 6.45, 7.00.

Page 87
Green train: 8, 10, 12, 14, 16, 18, 20.
Hidden numbers (from left to right): 3, 5, 8; 10, 2, 7; 1, 9, 6.
Red train: 40, 50, 60, 70, 80, 90, 100.
Hidden numbers (from left to right): 3, 6, 2; 4, 9, 10; 8, 1.

Page 88
Missing numbers are: 20, 25, 30, 35, 40, 45, 50.
Hidden numbers are (from left to right): 1, 3, 9; 5, 6, 2; 8, 4, 7. Left: 3 fives; right: 6 fives.

Page 89

Page 90
top row: 3 balls; middle row: 3 balls; bottom row: 2 balls.

Page 91
parrots: 2 twos and 3 twos; ducks: 3 threes and 4 threes; marbles: 3 fours, 2 fours and 4 fours.